St Mark's Gospel Carpet Page taken from Lindisfarne Gospels.

ISBN 978 - 0 - 9557396 - 0 - 6

Printed by Shiremoor Press Ltd,
Mylord Crescent
Camperdown Industrial Estate
Killingworth
Newcastle Upon Tyne
NE12 5UJ

Publisher S.J. Publishing
Farnham Close
Lemington
Newcastle Upon Tyne
NE15 8RG

Email: sjpublishing@myguide.net

Acknowledgements

My friend, Nicola Phelps, who first suggested that I write this book.

My life-long friend Steven McDonnell, who helped give me the inspiration and background knowledge when making a film on Oswald and Heavenfield.

My friend Jeanette Dunn, who suggested I make it a book for younger people.

My good friend Tom Hutchinson, for the original design work and encouragement throughout the book.

Dawn Rodgers of Yellow Tiger Design and Marketing Ltd for their extra design work, and print finishing.

Cyril McBrine for proofreading.

Lynn Stuart for advice and guidance.

Heather Russell, founder member of the Society for Editors and Proofreaders, for her advice.

Gary Clark for computer help.

My son Nathan (12), who helped a stressed dad through the process of completing this book, and all those people who have helped without knowing.

This book has been a labour of love,

Thank you all.

The author,
Steven Jemison, is a
singer, songwriter and storyteller
who has lived all his life in
Northumberland.

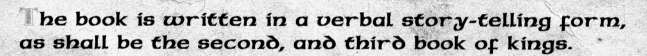

This book is a work of fiction based
on the historical figure of Oswald,
the First Overlord Godly King of
England.

The book is written in a verbal story-telling form,
as shall be the second, and third book of kings.

SCOTLAND

Picts

Iona   Irish
        Dairiada

Aberdeen

NORTH

Edinburgh

SEA

IRELAND
Dairiada

Ninian's Cave

Whithorn

Reghed

Bernicia

NORTHUMBRIA

Holy Island
(Lindisfarne)
Bamburgh
Hexham (Dinguardi)
Durham

Deira
York

WALES
Gwynedd

Mercia
Hatfield
R. Idle

R. Humber

Lindsey

Kent

R. Thames

Wessex   Sussex

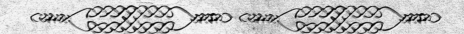

here was once a great castle and there was once a boy.

The boy was named Oswald. He was nine years old and lived in the castle with his mother and father and younger brother Oswy.

Oswald and his brother lived their lives as princes, free in the land of Northumbria. The castle was called Bamburgh after the children's great-great-grandmother, Bebba.

swald had many days of happiness playing in and around the castle with his brother.

Sometimes they would play tricks on their mother and father by wearing different veils and helmets over their heads and talking in different voices until their parents realized who they were.

They would also hide in the castle, playing hide-and-seek and leaving small treats for each other to find.

They had their own friends to play with, as there were hundreds of people in and around the castle, including their father's huge army of around five thousand men.

swald had an especially good friend called Saratus. The boys enjoyed playing on the seashore, making sandcastles just as you do today!

They would bury each other in the sand or go swimming together, lying on floating logs that they would tie to rocks on the shore so that they would not float away.

The two boys, who were the same age, grew up closely together and became the best of friends, even though they lived in different parts of the castle. Although Saratus and his family were poor, Oswald's father let them stay in the castle, so they could help with various jobs around the place.

ne day Oswald and Saratus were playing in the sand.

Oswald asked Saratus, 'Why are you my friend and always play with me?'
And Saratus said, 'Because I am your friend Oswald, am I not?'
'Well yes, but is it not just because I will be King some day?' asked Oswald.
'Don't be silly!' said Saratus. 'It is because you are my friend.'

Oswald knew that he was being honest as it sounded and felt like the truth. Oswald was pleased and it made him feel good. He put his faith in God.

 ust as Oswald and Saratus were playing, they saw a man walking along.

They watched him approach a small brown mound. The man realized it was a dead deer which he immediately started to drag away.

At that moment he was spotted by several of the king's soldiers, who immediately tied up the man and took him to the King.

 he King (Oswald's Father) said:

YOU ARE GUILTY OF KILLING ONE OF MY DEER!'

The man replied, 'Oh dear, dear, dear!' The King then said 'You shall leave this castle, never to return.'

Oswald was very upset at what had happened, and he tried to explain to his father that the man did not kill the deer, but his father would not listen.

This was another of Oswald's lessons in life, to know you can get into trouble for doing nothing wrong.

It was also a lesson for Saratus.

swald and Saratus, like most boys, enjoyed playing around the fire in the Great Hall, seeing how long it would take for different kinds of wood to burn and watching what happened.

And, as many people say, 'Children who play with fire get burnt.' Oswald surely did.

The piece of wood that Oswald was holding was covered in gluey sap from the wood, and stuck to his hand. The flames got nearer and they reached and burnt his right hand before he pulled it free with the other.

This was Oswald's greatest feeling of physical pain. He was still learning.

verything was fine until one day Oswald's father, Aethelfrith, was called away to protect his Northumbrian Kingdom from the king of Deira, called Edwin.

Edwin won the battle and killed Oswald's father at the River Idle.

So Oswald's mother and younger brother (Oswy) went with Oswald to their friends for safety on the west coast of Scotland to an island called Iona.

swald was now twelve and this meant he was old enough to take his sword and shield.

But before he left, he went to see his friend Saratus to say farewell and told Saratus that one day he would be back to see him and to take back his father's throne. On his way to Iona, Oswald walked, ran, rode on horseback and in a wagon pulled by four horses.

On this journey he also had to go on two small boats across the sea, first across to the Isle Of Mull, then from the Isle Of Mull to Iona (which is a very small island.)

hen Oswald got to Iona the first thing he noticed was that he did not understand what the people were saying as they were speaking old Irish and Scottish, which were not the same languages as those used today.

The people who lived on Iona were monks. Oswald was soon at work with them as they were teaching him about the Lord God. They were also giving him knowledge about the world and were teaching him to read books.

That was when he was not learning to fight, and learn to fight he surely did, as one day he might need to fight to claim his father's kingdom.

Oswald at the monks' house.

By the time he was thirteen, he had put away his childhood games and had been placed in charge of twelve boys just like himself to train them to fight.

They all soon became his friends, except one boy who was jealous of Oswald. His name was Ticnal - a small Irish boy - but Oswald tolerated him as he thought it was good for him to be tolerant of others. But he still had much love and respect from his friends, who also did not like Ticnal. They also had to be tolerant of him.

He would have drinks with his friends and have fun fights. But they were not bothered about who won amongst themselves.

hen Oswald was seventeen he was sent off with his friends and the army to fight in his first battle against a northern Pictish King.

Oswald and his friends fought well and won the battle. He then gained much respect from the monks and soldiers alike, and they put Oswald in command of the army.

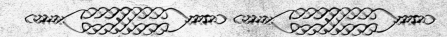

 he monks would travel down the west coast to **W**hithorn **P**riory, a large home they owned.

Oswald and his army were asked to go with them to protect them, and this they did. **H**e would always go out of his way to stop at a place called **N**inian's **C**ave, which is named after the monk who lived there, where he would find peace and comfort in prayer.

swald did not know, but Ticnal had been planning to have him killed.

Ticnal arranged for a small army to attack Oswald at Ninian's Cave. The army was returning to the Highlands of Scotland after meeting Cadwallon of Wales, who was one of Oswald's father's enemies. Oswald heard that they were planning to kill him and was waiting for them. He and his men fought hard and again won the battle. He then stayed at Whithorn Priory before going back to Iona, where he received a hero's welcome.

Oswald returned a hero, to the monks' house.

swald would sometimes go across the sea to Ireland with his army. There he would help Connad Cerr (one of the kings, who was his friend) to fight his enemies.

And when he wasn't fighting, he would visit his monk friends in the Irish Monastery.

By the time he was twenty-five years old he had won many battles and had much love and respect from the people he cared for. And for the next three years, there was peace on the west coast of Scotland until he was nearly twenty-eight years old. Then he got the news that his Uncle Edwin (who had killed Oswald's father) had, himself, been killed at Hatfield further south by King Cadwallon of Wales.

Oswald started to hear about bad things happening at his birthplace of Northumbria.

swald realized the task of saving the Kingdom was his responsibility.

He returned to Northumbria with his army. He met his old friend Saratus, as well as his younger brother Oswy, and many Northumbrians joined them to do battle against the mighty Cadwallon and his army at a place now called Heavenfield, which is on the Roman Wall, near Hexham.

 holy man, a monk called Bede, not long after the battle, wrote down what happened.

He said that Oswald made a wooden cross, and kneeling at the foot of the cross said:

Let us bow the knee and together pray
The almighty God living and true
That he will in his mercy
Save us from the proud and savage enemy
As he knows that he will have undertaken
A just war
For the salvation of our nation.

swald's army was greatly outnumbered, but they still defeated and killed Cadwallon and most of his army.

Oswald was then made King of Northumbria, becoming Overlord of the Irish, and of the Picts in Scotland. He was so pleased that his prayer to God had been heard, allowing him to win the battle.

swald brought monks with him from Iona when he returned to Northumbria, but they thought that Oswald's people did not want to know about God and returned to Iona.

So Oswald sent a message to Iona for a special monk to teach his United Kingdom about God. And they sent him a bishop monk named Aidan who was only twenty-five. Aidan came to Northumbria with some other monks to tell Oswald's people about God.

Oswald and Aidan at the Roman Wall

swald was so pleased with Aidan that he gave him the island of Lindisfarne across the bay from Bamburgh Castle. The island is known to this day as Holy Island.

On the island Aidan built a monastery as a home for his monks. Oswald and Saratus spent a lot of time together with Aidan to translate his stories of God for Oswald's people, who would not be able to understand Aidan, as he spoke in Irish.

Many years later there were many monasteries built in Northumbria to spread the word of God throughout the known world.

swald married an English princess called Cynegils, who came from Wessex. He became Overlord over the Kings of Lindsey and Kent and was the first true Godly King of all England.

Oswald was happy and his United Kingdom was at peace.

Many now believe him to be a Saint, for all the good things that he did.

An Deireadh

(The End)

Oswald's Castle Today

Holy Island Today

The Line of the Roman Wall Today

St Luke's Gospel Carpet Page taken from Lindisfarne Gospels.

Shelfmark/page: Cotton Nero D. IV, f.138v